Inclusion
Alphabet

KATHRYN JENKINS

ISBN: 978-1-7327404-2-6

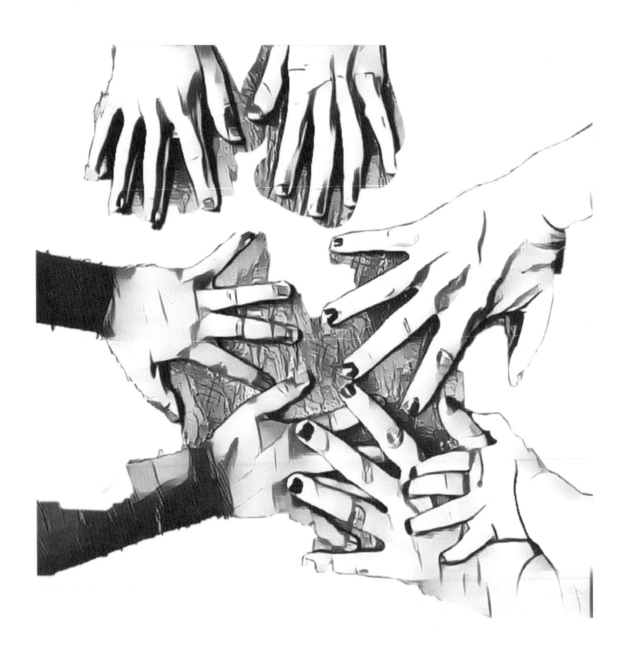

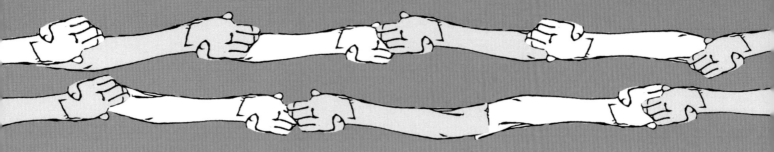

To my three little men,
May you always see the
power of inclusion.

Love, Mom

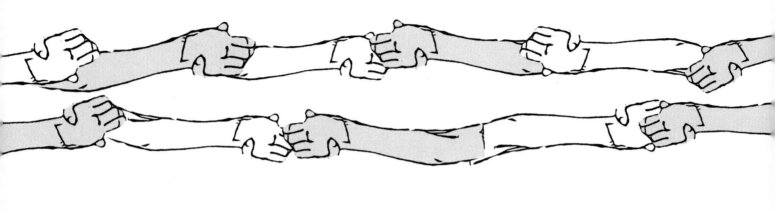

A

is for Acceptance

The little boy said,
"I accept that I
am different."

B

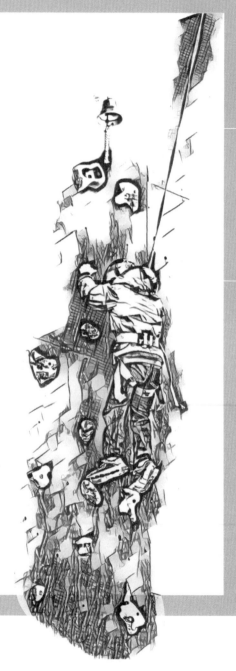

is for Bravery

The little boy's mom said, "You are brave and can try new things."

C

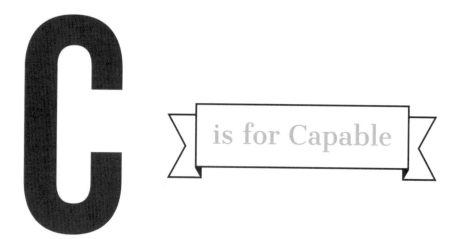

is for Capable

The friend of the little boy said, "Look!
I'm capable and so are you."

D

is for Different

The little girl realized
she was different too.

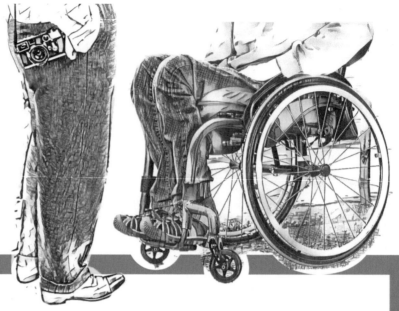

E

is for Empathy

A man down the street at the neighborhood park felt empathy for a stranger and asked, "How do you do it?"

F

The stranger said, "I forgive and let go. I focus on each day as a new opportunity."

G

is for Gratitude

The little boy's brother was grateful for a friend to play with.

H

is for Heart

He had a big heart and loved everyone unconditionally.

I

is for Inclusion

The little girl listened as her
teacher talked about inclusion.

J

is for Journey

And how it can be a journey that is different for everyone.

K

is for Kindness

The teacher said, "Inclusion is not about being in the same place; it's about being kind and then, adapting our plans to make room for everyone."

L

is for Listening

Another way to show
kindness is to listen to
people's feelings. The little
girl tried hard to listen to
those around her.

M

is for Mindful

As the man returned to the park and listened to the stranger talk about his life, he became mindful of the people around him.

N

is for Not Normal

"We aren't all that different from each other," he said. "We are not normal, but who wants to be normal?"

O

is for Open

He was open and excited. He saw
happiness all around him and decided
that he would look for ways to include
everyone.

P

is for Potential

The teacher told the little girl,
"Everyone can reach their full
potential with a little help".

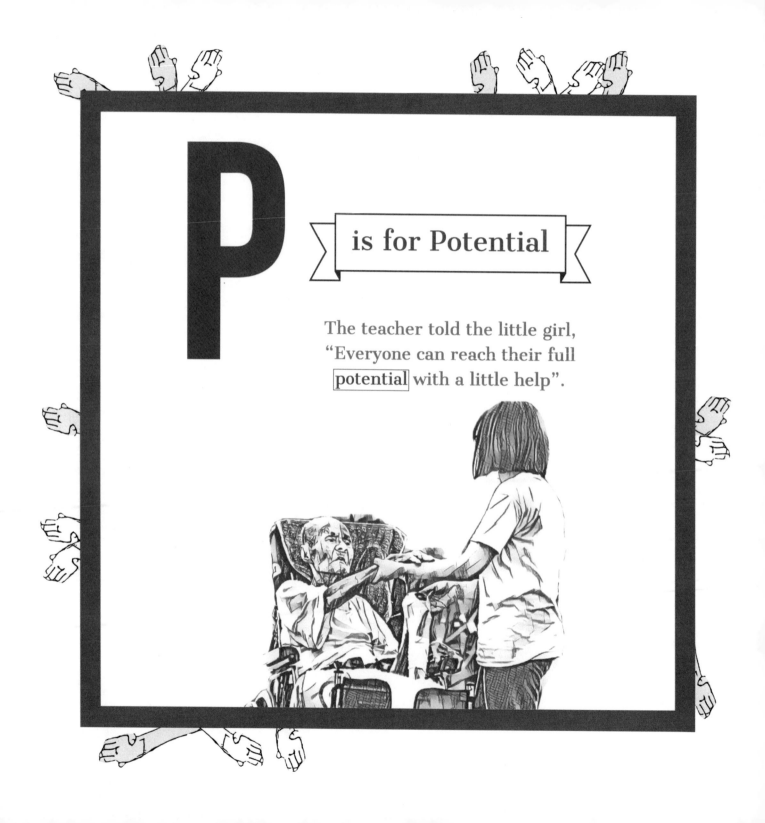

Q

The little boy walked home with his mom. "It will be better tomorrow. You have a lot of great qualities I admire in you," she said.

R

is for Respect

His mom talked about respect for others with a different skin color, a different gender, or different beliefs. The little boy's baby brother gave him a big hug.

S

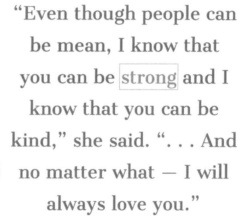

is for Strength

"Even though people can be mean, I know that you can be strong and I know that you can be kind," she said. ". . . And no matter what — I will always love you."

T

is for Teachable

"And one day those people who acted mean will be teachable, and they will learn. We can all learn."

U

is for Understanding

The little girl went to the park and met a new friend but the friend couldn't speak. She remembered what her teacher said about inclusion, and so, she chose to understand.

V

is for Value

Because we all have value.

W

is for Work

The two girls played without words.
They worked together as they went down
the slide. They giggled and laughed.

X

is for Xenial

As the little boy entered the park, he could hear a group of people singing, "Xenial! Be Xenial." He stopped and listened. It was a song he had never heard. The stranger spoke up, "It means to be hospitable and welcoming." He smiled and continued with his mom and baby brother.

Y

is for You

The two girls saw the little
boy playing alone.
"Would you like to play?"
they asked.

Z

is for Zeal

With **zeal** and excitement, the little boy nodded. Then he replied, "Can my little brother play too?"

INCLUSION DICTIONARY

Acceptance: the act or process of being open and receptive to something

Bravery: to exhibit courageous behavior

Capable: the ability to achieve

Different: not the same as another

Empathy: to understand or try to experience what other people are feeling and put yourself "in their shoes"

Forgiveness: the process of letting go of hurt or angry feelings caused by another individual or one's own self

Gratitude: a choice to feel thankful

Heart: a central organ in the body that pumps blood; it also refers to someone's character and their ability to love

Inclusion: the process of creating and finding opportunities for each person to reach their full potential regardless of race, religious beliefs, ethnicity, sexual identity, physical or psychological ailments, intelligence, differences, or other attributes that may set them apart from you.

Journey: the act of moving physically, mentally, or emotionally from one stage to another

Kindness: to show friendly, generous, and considerate behavior

Listening: taking notice and processing what someone says

Mindful: to be conscious and aware

Not Normal: different, and/or unique

Open: to be flexible with accepting change, and willing to learn

Potential: a prospective value you place on something or someone

Qualities: distinctive attributes someone possesses

Respect: a feeling of deep admiration for someone or something

Strength: a quality or attribute that resembles steadfastness and the ability to withstand great force

Teachable: the willingness to learn by listening and acting upon what is taught

Understanding: being aware of and having compassion for someone else

Value: seeing worth and determining potential

Work: putting effort towards something

Xenial: being hospitable and friendly to new people

You: referring to any person and acknowledging their existence

Zeal: showing excitement and energy

About the Author

KATHRYN JENKINS

Most of my time is spent making sure my kids don't stick lego building blocks up their noses. I am a mom to three young boys and I love it. When I do get a spare moment to myself, I sit down and I write or create something. I used several photo editing techniques to create the illustrations for this book. They were originally photographs that have now been edited into sketches. I am also the creator and constant voice for the @inclusion_project. I work on encouraging others to tell their stories and spread inclusion in the community where they live. I believe that we are what we say, what we do, what we think, what we make, and of course, what we read and so I'm thrilled to be joining the publishing world as a first time author. Inclusion Alphabet really came about while I was sitting in a school parking lot waiting for my son with special needs. As each child exited the school, anxiously looking for their ride home, it was easy to pick out the students with plenty of friends and family support. It was just as easy to see the children who were struggling and perhaps, alone. After jotting down a few things that day on a receipt in my car, I decided I was going to write this book because every child has worth and deserves an opportunity to succeed. It is thrilling to have others read something that I created and feel so strongly about. I currently reside in Woods Cross, Utah with my husband and kids. I want to thank the many family and friends who helped to make this possible for me.

@inclusion_project

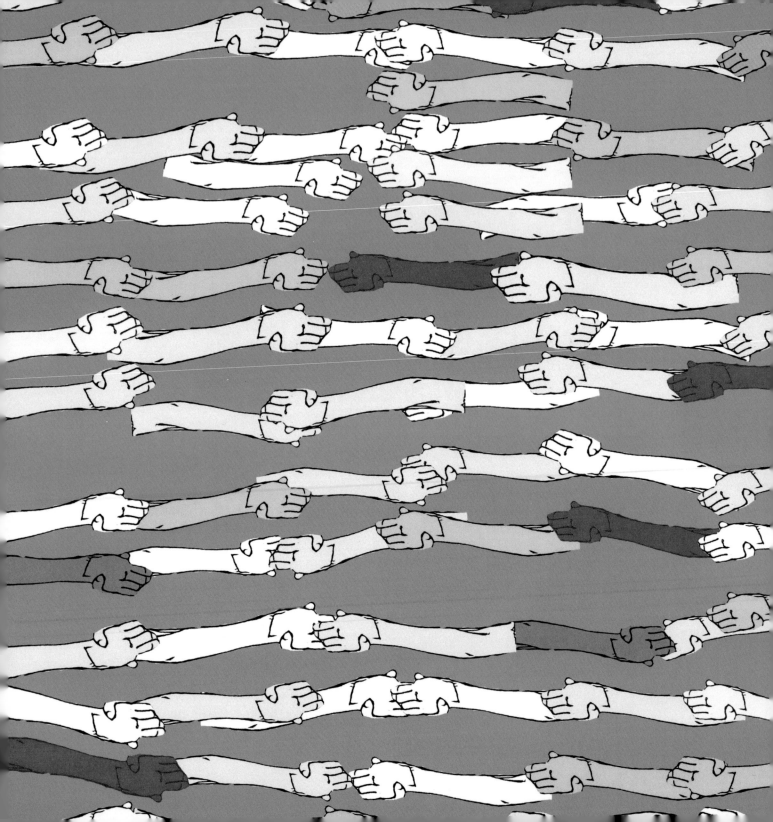

Made in the USA
Columbia, SC
30 December 2018